JUMP RIGHT IN
THE MUSIC CURRICULUM

J238

JUMP RIGHT IN
THE MUSIC CURRICULUM

CYNTHIA C. **TAGGART**   BETH M. **BOLTON**   ALISON M. **REYNOLDS**   WENDY H. **VALERIO**   EDWIN E. **GORDON**

DAVID G. WOODS
FIRST EDITION CO-AUTHOR

GIA PUBLICATIONS, INC
CHICAGO

Piano accompaniments by Bruce Taggart

"The Ant Dance" © 1975, Doug Nichol; "Autumn" © 1970, Canyon Press; "Bread in the Oven" © 1975, Doug Nichol; "Dhikr" © 1970, Canyon Press; "Echo Canon for Owls" © 1977, Schott Music Corp.; "The Goat" © 1970, Canyon Press; "Grandma" © 1974, Doug Nichol; "Grandma Bear from Delaware" © 1986, Jack Prelutsky from *Ride a Purple Pelican* used by permission of Greenwillow Books; "The Grasshopper and the Elephant" © 1974, Doug Nichol; "Happiness" by A.A. Milne from *When We Were Very Young* by A.A. Milne © 1924 by E.P. Dutton, renewed 1952 by A.A. Milne, used by permission of Dutton's Children's Books, a division of Penguin Putnam, Inc.; "Hello Everybody" © 1955, Plymouth Music Co., Inc.; "I Want to Be a Circus Clown" © 1978, Doug Nichol; "Keep the Earth Clean" © 1974, Doug Nichol; "Let's Play in the Snow" © 1978, Doug Nichol; "Little Train" © , Grace C. Nash; "Popcorn" © 1974, Doug Nichol; "Sam, Sam, The Butcher Man" © 1975, Doug Nichol; "Top of My Head" © 1976, Doug Nichol; "Witch of Willowby Wood" © 1983, Mary Goetze.

Cover design: The Kantor Group

Copyright © 2000, GIA Publications, Inc.
7404 S. Mason Ave., Chicago, IL 60638
1.800.GIA.1358 or 1.708.496.3800 • www.giamusic.com

J238
ISBN: 1-57999-064-9
Printed in U.S.A.

CONTENTS

Fall

3

Hello Everybody

Eunice Holsaert
Charity Bailey

1. Hel - lo, ev - 'ry-bod - y, yes in - deed,
2. Good - bye, ev - 'ry-bod - y, yes in - deed,

yes in - deed, yes in - deed. Let's make mu - sic,
yes in - deed, yes in - deed. Stay well and hap - py,

yes in - deed, Yes in - deed my friend!
yes in - deed, Yes in - deed my friend!

Moving Our Bodies

Hop Old Squirrel

Traditional

Hop, old squirrel, ei-dle-dum, ei-dle-dum,

Hop, old squirrel, ei-dle-dum, dum,

Hop, old squirrel, ei-dle-dum, ei-dle-dum,

Hop old squirrel, ei-dle-dum dee.

The Squirrel

Transcribed by
Kyungsil Jung

Whis - ky, fris - ky, hop - pi - ty hop Up he goes to the

tree top. Whir - ly, twir - ly, round and a - round

Down he scam - pers to the ground.

Button You Must Wander

Traditional

But - ton you must wan - der, wan - der, wan - der,

But - ton you must wan - der, Ev - 'ry - where.

Bright eyes will find you, Sharp eyes will find you.

But - ton you must wan - der, Ev - 'ry - where.

Can you make a statue with your body?

Autumn Leaves

Beth M. Bolton

Au - tumn leaves, au - tumn leaves, au - tumn leaves are

Fine

fal - ling. Blow - ing in the wind.

Danc - ing in the sky. Win - ter's come a -

D.C. al Fine

gain. Wish that I could fly.

Witch of Willowby Wood

There was an old witch of Willowby Wood
and a weird, wild witch was she.
With hair that was snarled
and hands that were gnarled,
and a ricketty, clicketty, knee.
She could jump to the moon and back,
but this I never did see.

© 1983, Mary Goetze.

Jack O' Lantern

Pumpkin patch, pumpkin patch
I'm looking for a pumpkin
in a pumpkin patch
Here is one, nice and fat
Turn into a jack-o-lantern just like that!

Echo Canon for Owls

Follow My Leader

Native American

Fol - low my lead - er,

Wher - e'er he goes, What he'll

do next, No - bod - y knows.

Turkey Song

Wisconsin

As I came o-ver yon-der hill I spied a might-y tur-key. He flapped his wings and he spread his tail, And his feet looked aw-ful dirt-y. Fol-link-a-ti-dy, Fol-de-link-a-ti-dy-o, Fol-link-a-ti-dy, And his feet looked aw-ful dirt-y.

The Old Woman and the Pig

Ways to Move

Streamer Dance

Circle Dance

Walk

Gallop

Winter

Grandma

Anonymous

Doug Nichol

1. Grand - ma has a hab - it of
2. Grand - pa does - n't mind it though, as

chew - ing in her sleep. She
long as he's a - sleep. He

chews on Grand - pa's whis - kers and
says he's on - ly thank - ful she

thinks it's shred - ded wheat.
does - n't chew his feet.

Hanukkah

Things That Jingle

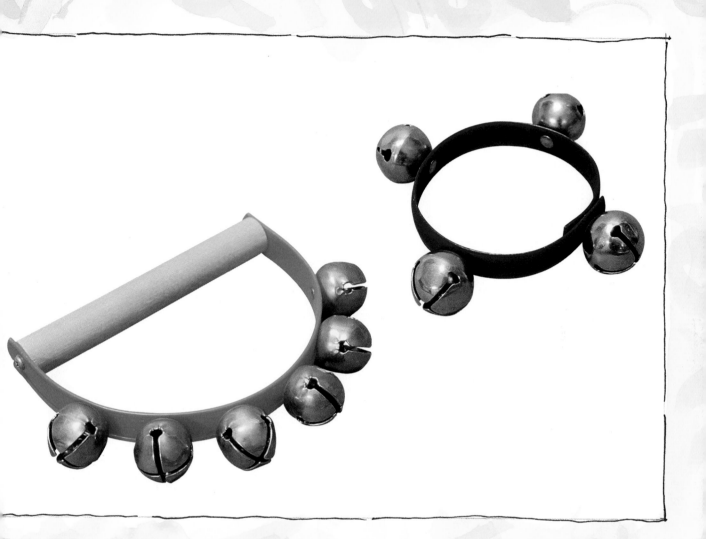

Let's Play In The Snow

Three Craws

Fros - ty   morn - ing.

Grizzly Bear

Traditional

mf

Griz-zly bear, a   griz-zly bear, Is sleep-ing in a cave.

pp

Please be ver-y   qui-et,   Ver-y, ver-y   qui-et.

ff

If you wake him,   If you shake him,   He gets ver-y MAD!

35

Bread In The Oven

Traditional
Adapted by Eric Nichols

1. Bread in the ov - en, bak - ing,
2. Cake in the ov - en, bak - ing,

bak - ing, bak - ing, Bread in the
bak - ing, bak - ing, Cake in the

ov - en bak - ing bak - ing for our din - ner.
ov - en bak - ing, bak - ing for our sup - per.

Hungry

Hungarian

Hi! Ho! Winds now blow! Hun - gry girls must

eat you know. Roast goose leg is

tast - ed, Not a bit is wast - ed.

At The Cozy Hearth

Postman

Sam, Sam, The Butcher Man

Anonymous

Doug Nichol

Sam, Sam, the but - cher man

Washed his face in a fry - ing pan,

Combed his hair with a wag - on wheel,

Died with a tooth - ache in his heel.

Copyright © 1975 Doug Nichol

You Will Never Find Me

Mi   Do   La

Love Somebody

Love   some - bod - y

America

Henry Carey

Samuel Francis Smith

My coun - try, 'tis of thee, Sweet land of lib - er - ty, Of thee I sing. Land where my fa - thers died, Land of the Pil - grims' pride, From ev - 'ry— moun - tain side Let— free - dom ring.

America The Beautiful

O beautiful for spacious skies,
For amber waves of grain.
For purple mountain majesties
Above the fruited plain!
America! America! God shed His grace on thee
And crown thy good with brotherhood,
from sea to shining sea!

O beautiful for Pilgrim feet,
Whose stern, impassioned stress
A thoroughfare for freedom beat,
Across the wilderness.
America! America! God mend thine ev'ry flaw.
Confirm thy soul in self-control,
Thy liberty in law.

Twinkle, Twinkle Little Star

Traditional

Twin - kle, twin - kle, lit - tle star,

Fine

How I won - der what you are.

Up a - bove the world so high,

D.C. al Fine

Like a dia - mond in the sky,

Star Light, Star Bright

Traditional

Star light, star bright, First star I see to-night.

Wish I may, wish I might, Have this wish I wish to-night.

49

Things That Ring

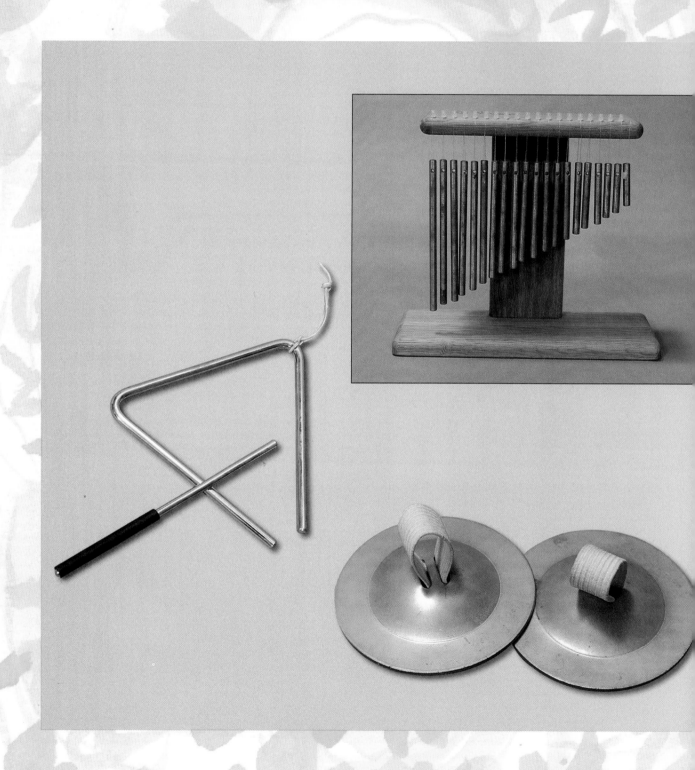

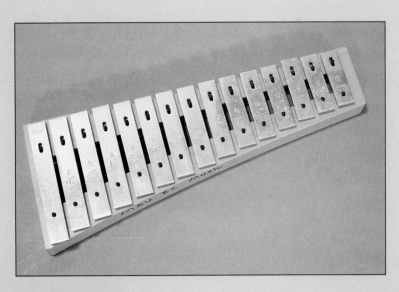

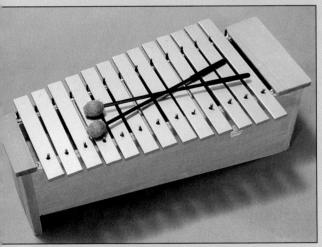

51

The Orchestra

Photo Copyright © Chicago Symphony Orchestra

I'm Gonna Put On My Walkin' Shoes

Traditional

I'm gon - na put, put, put on my walk - in' shoes,— I'm gon - na but - but - but-ton up my coat;—— I'm gon - na walk, walk, walk where there's things to see, And if you want to you can walk with me.

How can
we walk?

Cape Dorset

Eskimo Lullaby

1. Hi, lit – tle ti – ny daugh – ter,

Hi, lit – tle ti – ny daugh – ter.

2. We have a gift, a girl child,
   We have a gift, a girl child.

3. She doesn't know a thing yet,
   She doesn't know a thing yet.

56

Ally Bally

Scottish

Gently

Al - ly bal - ly, al - ly bal - ly bee,

Sit - tin' on your dad - dy's knee.

Greet - in' for a wee pen - ny, To

buy some Coul - ter's can - dy.

Spring

Irish Tune from County Derry

Percy Grainger

Things That Click

Happiness

A. A. Milne

John had Great big Wa-ter-proof Boots on;

John had a Great big Wa-ter-proof Hat;

John had a Great big Wa-ter-proof Mack-in-tosh—And

that (Said John) Is That.

How would a grasshopper move?

How would an elephant move?

Happy Monkey

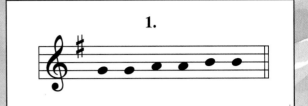

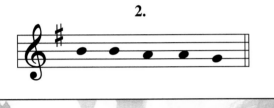

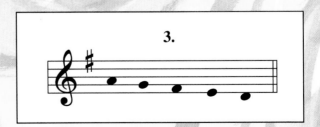

Lazy Bones

Kimigayo

Japanese National Anthem

Ki - mi - ga - yo — wa   Chi - yo - ni,—
(Kih - mih - gah - yoe— wah,   Chee - yoe - ni—

Ya - chi - yo - ni   sa - za - re - i - shi - no,
Yah - chee - yoe - nee   sah - zah - ray - ee - shee - noe,

I - wa - o - to   na - ri - te
Ee - wah - oh - toh   nah - ree - teh

ko - ke - no   mu - su — ma - de.
Koh - kee - noh   moo - soo — mah - day.)

Summer

Frog Song

My Little Ducklings

Closet Key

Traditional

I have lost the clos-et key, In my La-dy's gar-den.

I have lost the clos-et key, In my La-dy's gar-den.

78

Lock The Dairy Door

Children's Round

Lock the dair - y door, — Lock the dair - y door.

"Chic - kle, chac - kle, chee, I have - n't got the key."

Banbury Cross

Transcribed by
Cynthia Crump Taggart

Ride a big horse to Ban-bu-ry Cross to see a fine la - dy up-

on a white horse. Rings on her fin - gers, bells on her toes,

She shall have mu - sic where - e - ver she goes.

Ride O, Ride O

Bouncing

Swedish

Ri - da, ri - da, ran - ka,— Häst - en het - tar
Ride - o, ride - o, ride - o, up - on your horse a -

Blan - ka, Vart— skall vi ri - da?
stride o, Which way shall we ride - o?

Jag— skaut och fri - a, Til en li - ten pi - ga.
To the coun - try - side - o, To find a fair bride - o.

Chula La Manana

Grasshoppers Three

Traditional

Grass-hop-pers three a-fid-dl-ing went, Hey, ho,

nev-er be still! They paid no mon-ey to-ward their rent, But

all day long with el-bow bent, They fid-dled a tune called

Ril-la-by-ri-la-by, Fid-dled a tune called Ril-la-by-ril.

Ant Dance

Doug Nichol

Swing it!

I went for a walk a week a-go to-day. I

got kind of tired so I set my-self down. I ac-ci-dent-ly sat on a

hill of ants and they made me do the Ant - sy, Ant-sy Dance.

Refrain

Bum bum bum bum *etc.*

What kind of dance would you do?

Cowboy's Gettin' Up Holler

American Cowboy Song

Expressively

Wake up, Ja-cob, Day's a break-in',_____

Peas in the pot and the hoe-cake's bak-in'!_____

Ear-ly in the morn-ing, Al-most day,___ If you

don't come soon, Gon-na throw it all a-way.___ (Hit on pan) Wake up!

Git Along Little Dogies

Stars & Stripes Forever

Sally Go 'Round the Sun

Traditional

Sal-ly, go 'round the sun, Sal-ly go 'round the moon, Sal-ly go 'round the chim-ney top Ev – 'ry af – ter – noon.

Round and Round

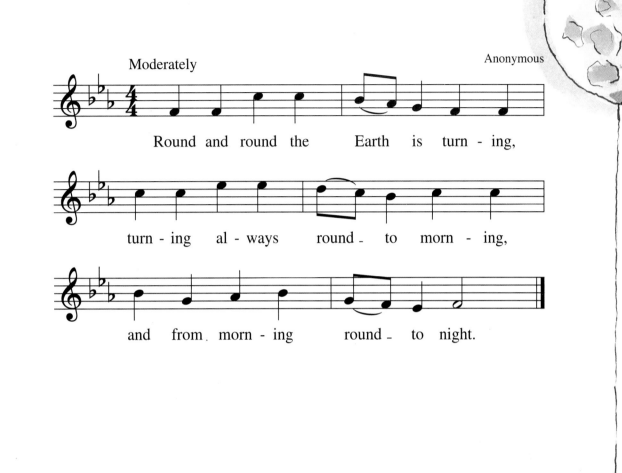

Moderately

Anonymous

Round and round the Earth is turn - ing,

turn - ing al - ways round to morn - ing,

and from morn - ing round to night.

Index